Covers the new updated scheme of work

G000139271

It's Another Ace Book from CGP

It's chock-full of questions that are carefully designed to make sure you know all the <u>really important stuff</u> about 'Gases Around Us' in Year Five Science.

And we've had a really good stab at making it funny — so you'll actually <u>want to use it</u>.

Simple as that.

CGP are just the best

The central aim of Coordination Group Publications is to produce top quality books that are carefully written, beautifully presented and marvellously funny — whilst always making sure they exactly cover the National Curriculum for each subject.

And then we supply them to as many people as we possibly can, as <u>cheaply</u> as we possibly can.

Buy our books — they're ace

Contents

Answers to the questions are on the back of the Pull-out Poster in the centre of the book.

Published by Coordination Group Publications Ltd.

Contains Strange Purple Gas

Contributors:
Angela Billington BA (Hons), MPhil
Chris Dennett BSc (Hons)
Lindsay Jordan BSc (Hons)
Tim Major
Katherine Stewart BA (Hons)
Claire Thompson BSc
Tim Wakeling BA (Hons), GIMA
James Paul Wallis BEng (Hons)

With thanks to Taissa Csáky BA (Hons) for the proofreading.
ISBN 1-84146-268-3
Groovy website: www.cgpbooks.co.uk
Jolly bits of clipart from CorelDRAW
Printed by Elanders Hindson, Newcastle upon Tyne.

Differences Between Solids and Liquids

This page is all about <u>solids</u> and <u>liquids</u>. It shouldn't be too hard — you've seen all this before.

Q1 Take a look at these pictures and write the names in the table under SOLID or LIQUID.

cake

milkshake

water

book

rock

soup

SOLID	LIQUID
....	....
....	....
....	....

Gavin found out the difference between solids and liquids the hard way.

Q2 Now write the names of the objects next to the right headings — you'll need to write each object next to three of the headings. I've done one already to start you off.

Will flow: *Milkshake* , ... , ...

Won't flow: .... , ... , ...

Will take the shape of the container it's put in:

Milkshake , ... , ...

Will keep its own shape when it's put in a container:

.... , ... , ...

Can be held between your fingers:

.... , ... , ...

Can't be held between your fingers:

Milkshake , ... , ...

How to make a milkshake — put a cow on a bouncy castle...

You need to be able to tell the difference between solids and liquids — easy. You've got to know that liquids can flow, but solids can't. It's not rocket science, but this is only page 1. It gets harder.

Air is Real

You can't <u>see</u> air, but that doesn't mean that it isn't there.
In fact, it's <u>all around</u> you. So every time you move, you're moving <u>through</u> air.

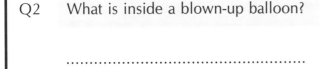

Q1 What is air? Tick ✔ the right answer.

A space with nothing in it. ☐ A substance that you can see. ☐

A substance all around you that you can't see. ☐

Q2 What is inside a blown-up balloon?

....

Q3 What do you breathe?

....

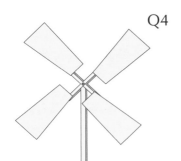

Q4 a) What happens when you blow on a paper windmill?

....

b) Why does that happen? Circle the right answer.

The sails try to move out of the draught because they're cold.

The air pushes on the sails.

The wind doesn't make any difference, so the windmill doesn't do anything.

You never blow quite straight, so you always blow the sails to one side, so they all move to the left.

Something's wrong here...

Jasmine showed Max how important air was by letting down his airbed.

<u>Air — not what you 'ave on your 'ead...</u>

This is all about the fact that air <u>isn't</u> nothing — it's a darn important substance. You'd have difficulty breathing without it, that's for sure. That makes it pretty important in my books.

Air is Real

You know how wind <u>pushes</u> against kites and umbrellas — this is the same kind of thing.

Q1   If you just jumped out of a plane, you'd fall really quickly and hit the ground too hard.

a)   If you jumped out of a plane with a parachute, would you fall more quickly or more slowly?

....

b)   Why? Tick ✔ the right answer.

Because you'd weigh more. ☐

Because the air would be pushing up against the parachute. ☐

Because the air would be pushing the parachute down. ☐

Q2   a)   Fill in the blanks in these sentences. Choose from the words on the right.

I have a toy boat with sails in my garden pond. On a .... day, the boat doesn't move. On a .... day, the boat moves really fast. That's because the .... is pushing against the sails. Wind is just .... that's moving.

still
windy
wind
air

b)   If I put bigger sails on my toy boat, would it move more quickly or more slowly?

....

c)   Why is that? Circle the right answer.

Because bigger sails will have more wind pressing against them.

Because bigger sails make it heavier, so it goes more slowly.

Because bigger sails make it look like a bigger boat, and bigger boats always go faster.

Air Trivia

Space shuttles use parachutes when they're landing to slow down, so they don't crash off the runway.

Where do you keep airtights? — In an airtight container...

Wind blowing against a sail, and air slowing a parachute down, are two good examples to show how air can show you it's there. If you go outside on a windy day, you'll feel air blowing on you too.

<u>*Air Has Weight*</u>

You might not think that air <u>weighs</u> anything (after all, you can't pick
it up and put it on some scales) but it <u>does</u> weigh something.

I did an experiment to find out whether a balloon weighs more when it's blown up or let down.
I took a balloon that wasn't blown up and weighed it on a set of electronic scales.
Then I blew it up very hard and weighed it again.

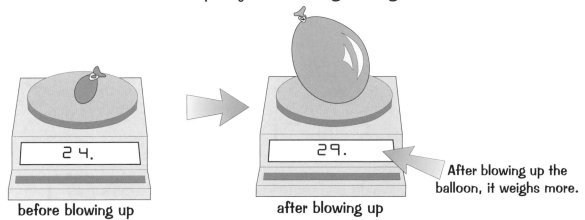

before blowing up

after blowing up

After blowing up the
balloon, it weighs more.

Q1   What is all squashed up in the blown-up balloon that makes it weigh more?

....

Q2   Fill in the blanks in these sentences, using the words in the balloon on the right.

Air is a .... and it has .... It's hard to

notice this because air is very .... The experiment

with the scales and balloons showed that air has weight, because the

balloon with .... squashed in it weighed

.... than the balloon with no air squashed in it.

light

more

weight

gas

air

Q3   Daisy the black and white diver has two air tanks. One is
empty, and the other is crammed full of air. Will they both
weigh the same? If not, which one will weigh more?

....

<u>*Weight a minute — this is heavy stuff...*</u>

It makes sense that air has weight — it would be weird for it to exist but weigh nothing.
When it's squashed up like in a blown-up balloon, it's more tightly packed so it weighs more.

Solids With Air In Them

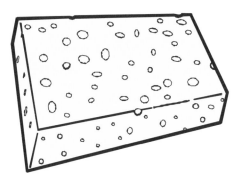

Some solids have holes in them. This page is about them.
OK, it doesn't sounds terrifically exciting, but it is fairly easy.

Q1 Here's a sponge. Is it a solid or a liquid?
Write "solid" or "liquid" on the dots.

....

Q2 In this close-up view of the sponge you
can see all the holes in it. What is in
the holes? Tick the right answer.

Stone ☐   Soil ☐

Air ☐   Treacle ☐

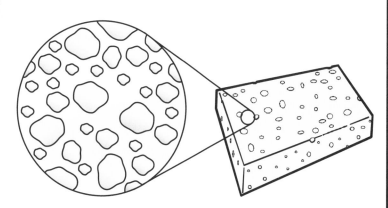

Q3 This is a close-up view of a pile of soil.
It's made up of little bits of solid, with spaces
in between them. What do you think is in
the spaces? Write your answer on the dots.

....

"There's a big
Bob-shaped
hole in this soil,"
thought Bob.

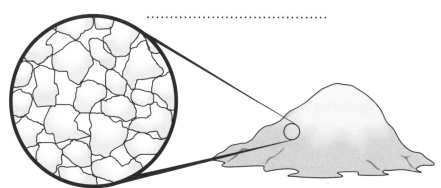

Sponge? — I prefer chocolate cake...

Everyone always says that solids don't change shape, but it just isn't quite true. Well, next time
someone says it to you, you can look really clever and say "Aha, but what about a sponge?"

MINI-PROJECT

Solids With Air In Them

This is an experiment to see what happens when you put a sponge under water and squeeze it.

The chefs used the wrong kind of sponge...

<u>Equipment</u> you will need:

A sponge.

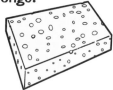

A bowl of water.

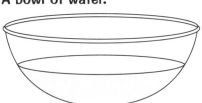

<u>Method</u> for doing the experiment:

Hold the sponge under the water, and squeeze it. Watch carefully to see what happens.

Q1   Do this experiment. What did you see when you squeezed the sponge under the water?

....

....

Q2   What was it that came out of the spaces when you squeezed the sponge? (Hint: The last page was about how sponges have spaces in them.)

....

Q3   Put the sponge under the water again, and squeeze it.
Then let go, so it goes back to its normal shape underwater.
What is in the spaces now? Write out the right answer.

Nowadays, most sponges are made in factories, but in the old days sponges were made from the skeletons of a kind of animal that lives in the sea.

| air | water | sponge | glass |

....

Can I have £5? — that's a different type of sponging...

Phew — this science is hard work, with all these experiments and squeezing sponges in a bowl.
OK, so it's easy, but it's still an experiment so you've got to do it carefully — don't bodge it.

Solids With Air In Them

This experiment is to find out what happens when you pour water onto a solid that's made of little bits.

Always wash your hands after you've touched soil.

<u>Equipment</u> you will need:

A jar of marbles.

A jar of sand.

A jar of soil.

A jug of water.

Put the sand and soil in gently — don't squash and squeeze them in.

If you are collecting soil, get an adult to help you choose a good place to find the soil — and watch out for rubbish or glass.

<u>Method</u> for doing the experiment:

Pour water into a jar gently. Watch what happens while you pour.
Stop pouring, and watch what happens. Then fill in the table to say what you saw.

Q1   Do the experiment like I've said above, for each of the jars, and write down what you see in this table.

	When I was pouring	Just after I stopped pouring
Marbles		
Sand		
Soil		

Doctor doctor I feel like a bridge.

What's come over you?

Three cars and a bus.

Douglas had lost his marbles.

Q2   You might have seen bubbles coming out.
What do you think the bubbles were made of?

(Hint: Think about what was in the spaces before you poured on the water.)   ....

Q3   Fill in the gaps in these sentences. Choose from the words in the bubbles.
You'll need to use some of the words more than once, and you don't need all of them.

When you pour .... onto marbles, it goes into the spaces and pushes out

the .... , which comes to the surface in .... Powders like

sand and soil are also made up of bits of solid with .... between them.

When you pour water on .... it's the same as with marbles — bubbles of

.... are pushed out by the .... and rise to the surface. The

bubbles keep coming to the surface until all the .... is pushed out.

air

bubbles

water

powders

steam

glue   soap

Solids With Air In Them

Sometimes when you do an experiment, you can get a result that you didn't expect.

Q1 Look back over the experiments on the last two pages. Were you surprised by the results?

....

Q2 What's the best way to check that you got the right results? Tick one box.

☐ Do the experiments again, but this time without looking.

☐ Do the experiments again in the same way as before.

☐ Phone the Prime Minister at 10 Downing Street.

Q3 Do the experiment from page 7 again, in exactly the same way as before. Make sure you use dry marbles, sand and soil. Write down your results in the table below.

	When I was pouring	Just after I stopped pouring
Marbles		
Sand		
Soil		

Q4 Look at the results you got above, and the results you got last time. Were they the same?

....

MONDAY

TUESDAY

WEDNESDAY

THURSDAY

FRIDAY

Liz and her brother loved doing the same experiment again and again.

Projects, experiments — these are testing times...

5 rules for experiments — read the instructions carefully, follow the instructions carefully, collect the results carefully, write down the results carefully, think about the results carefully. So <u>take care</u>.

Solids With Air In Them

If you get a surprising result, the best thing to do might be to
do the experiment again, and see if you get the same result again.

Q1   Why is it often helpful to do experiments more than once? Tick the 3 right answers.

☐   Because you might have made a mistake with the first experiment.

☐   So you get different results — then you can choose the results you like best.

☐   If you get the same results twice, you can say you probably got the right results.

☐   It makes it last longer.

☐   If you get different results, you know you've done something wrong
somewhere, so you need to do it a few more times to check.

☐   If you get different results each time, you can definitely
say that the second results were the right ones.

☐   Because you always forget to write
down the results the first time.

Mmm. Now I'll eat another bar,
and see if that tastes good too...

Bertha wanted to do this
experiment again...

Q2   Look back at the experiments on the last 3 pages. Write down
at least one thing that you found out from each experiment.

Sponge experiment: ....
....
....

The experiments with
marbles, sand and soil: ....
....
....

Repeat your experiments — your experiments your experiments...

You know the last page said that there were 5 rules to doing experiments.... well I've found
another — Rule Number 6: "do experiments more than once in case the 1st result was squiffy."

Testing How Much Air is In Soil

In soil, you get air in between all the bits. There are different types of soil and they don't all have the same amount of air inside them. You can test different soils to see which has more air inside it.

Q1 For this experiment, you start off by putting 100ml of 3 different types of soil into 3 measuring beakers. Look at these pictures and descriptions of experiments. Circle the one you think is the right one for finding out which soil has the most air trapped inside.

Pour 10ml of washing-up liquid onto each soil in turn, timing how long air bubbles come out of the soil. The soil that bubbles the longest has the most air in it.

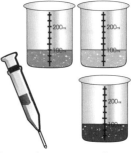

Take a plastic tipped syringe and stick it into each beaker in turn, using it to suck the air out of the soil. The amount of air you've sucked out tells you how much air was in the soil.

Pour water from a measuring jug onto the soil until the water reaches the 100ml mark and no more bubbles are coming out of the soil.

You should start with 500ml of water each time you begin pouring it on a soil. The amount of water that you poured in is the same as the amount of air that was in there before.

Q2 When you've done the experiment, how would you measure how much air had been in the soil? Tick the right answer.

Always start with 500ml of water in the cylinder to pour over the soil. When the soil has stopped bubbling and the water has settled at the 100ml mark, see how much water is left in the cylinder. Take this number away from 500 and you'll get the amount of air in the soil, measured in ml.

Always start with 500ml of water in the cylinder to pour over the soil. Pour the water on at a steady rate, timing how long in seconds it takes for the water to reach the 100ml mark and the soil to stop bubbling. Take this number away from 500 and the answer will be the amount of air in the soil, measured in ml.

Always start with no air in the syringe. Pull the plunger on the syringe, until you can't pull it any more. The amount of air in the syringe is the same as the amount of air in the soil, measured in ml.

Air in soil — lucky for worms blowing up balloons...

It's weird — you don't think about soil having air in it. But then I suppose all the things that live in the soil, like moles and worms, must have some way of breathing. Or they wouldn't last long...

Testing How Much Air is In Soil

For the soil experiment to work properly it has to be a <u>fair test</u>. If it isn't a fair test the results won't be any good. A fair test is keeping everything the same apart from the thing you are testing.

Q1 There were 3 things done to make the soil experiment on the last page a fair test. I've done one for you — write down the other two.

① ....

② ....

③ *All 3 beakers were the same shape and size.*

...But making it a fair test and making sure your results are accurate are slightly different things.

Q2 What could you do to check the experiment was accurate?

....

Jerry's soil experiment went a little bit wrong.

Q3 How could you make the experiment even more accurate? Put a tick next to the right answer.

Check all your equipment carefully before you start to make sure it is not broken, and check it again at the end to make sure the equipment is still not broken. ☐

Use a different amount of soil in each cylinder, one with 100ml, one with 200ml and another with 300ml. Then compare the three different results. ☐

Get all the soils from exactly the same place so it's a fair test. ☐

Repeat the test in exactly the same way a few times, and take an average of the results. ☐

Use at least six different types of soil for the experiment to give a bigger range and a better comparison. ☐

A fair test has nothing to do with the fairground.

Roll-up! Roll-up! Any type of soil that makes the bell ring, wins a prize.

A fare test — checking the cost of bus tickets...

Like any other experiment, you have to make sure it's a <u>fair test</u>. Only change one thing — if you had different sized beakers, you wouldn't know what changed the results — the beakers or the soil.

Testing How Much Air is In Soil

I've done an experiment just like the one on page 10, to
find out how much air is trapped in different types of soil.

Q1   Here's a table showing the results of the experiment. I've written in how
much water I started with and how much was left when the water reached
the 100ml mark and the soil stopped bubbling. Fill in the last column.

Type of soil	Volume of water at start	Volume of water at end	Volume of water in soil
Clay	500 ml	490 ml	ml
Sandy	500 ml	460 ml	ml
Normal	500 ml	480 ml	ml

Remember: to work
this out you have to
take the amount of
water at the end away
from the amount of
water at the start.

Q2   Write down which soil has the most air and which has the least air.
What does that tell you about the number or size of the gaps in the different types of soil?

....

....

....

....

....

OK lads, that's almost enough.

BIG HOLE PLAN

Clive thought he needed
more space in the soil
than normal worms.

Q3   Why do you think it might be more helpful to animals that
live in the soil if the soil has bigger gaps (or more gaps) in it?

....

....

....

Need sandy soil? — good excuse for a trip to the beach...

Darlington football ground was too soggy. They bought tons of worms to get more gaps in the soil, to
help water drain through. But they all drowned. Makes sense — loads of water, no air to breathe.

KS2 Science Answers — Gases Around Us

Page 14 Different Gases

Q1:

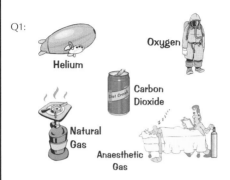

Page 15 Oxygen

Q1: a) It doesn't taste of anything.

b) Oxygen.

c) It is produced by plants.

d) flying high in aeroplanes, deep sea divers or people who have trouble breathing.

  Any answer giving an activity where people need more oxygen is ok.

Q2: Photosynthesis

Page 16 Evaporation

Q1: china dish ✓

plastic bowl ✓

Q2: It has evaporated - it's turned into a gas and gone into the air.

Page 17 Evaporation

The wording for any of the answers on this page could be different as long as the answers mean the same as the ones below.

Q1: a) They become dry.

b) The water on the clothes evaporates.

Q2: a) The water has evaporated off the clothes.

b) Because the water from the clothes is in the air.

Q3: The water has evaporated.

Page 18 Smells

Q1: Paint ✓   hot chocolate ✓   perfume ✓

Q2: Answer should be something like: It will disappear; It will evaporate.

Q3: a) Because none of the perfume had evaporated and so there was none in the air to go up your nose. (Or any answer that means the same.)

b) Because it would take some time for the perfume to travel through the big room to reach you. (Or any answer that means the same.)

Page 19 Smells

Q1: So you know they're there and can stop yourself breathing any in. ✓

Q2: Natural gas is **DANGEROUS** if it leaks.
It **BURNS** really easily, so if a load of gas leaked into a room and someone walked in and lit a **MATCH**, it could cause an **EXPLOSION**. If there was a gas leak in your house, you would **SMELL** the gas and could get out of the house and tell someone, so that the leak could be fixed.

Q3: So that if there is a leak people can smell it and get themselves out of danger and warn someone to come and fix it. (This can be worded differently as long as it means the same thing.)

Page 20 Solids, Liquids and Gases

Q1: a) No   b) No   c) Yes

d) It gets smaller

Q2: **SOLIDS** and **LIQUIDS** can't be squashed very easily — they stay the same size if you try to **SQUASH** them. **GASES** are much easier to squash — the same amount can always fit into a **SMALLER** space with a bit of pushing and squeezing.

Page 21 Solids, Liquids and Gases

Q1: a) The water will **POUR OUT**.

b) The smoke will **FLOW OUT IN ALL DIRECTIONS**.

Q2: a) It stays in the bottle. (Or any answer that means the same.)

b) Flow out in all directions. (Or any answer that means the same.)

Page 22 Solids, Liquids and Gases

Q1:

Wooden Block   Purple Gas   Water

Q2:

	Change in Shape	Change in Size	Does it flow? If so, which direction?
Wood	No change in shape	same	Doesn't flow — just falls
Purple Gas	Fills the bucket	bigger	Flows in all directions
Water	Fills bottom of bucket	same	Flows downwards

Page 23 Revision Pages

Q1: A substance all around you that you can't see.   ✓

Q2: Captain Birdsfeet is sailing his boat. On a **STILL** day, the boat doesn't move. On a **WINDY** day, the boat moves really fast. That's because the **WIND** is pushing against the sails. Wind is just **AIR** that's moving.

Q3: Air is a **GAS** and it has **WEIGHT**. It's hard to notice this because air is very **LIGHT**. A balloon with air squashed in it weighs **MORE** than one with no air squashed in it.

Q4:

Q5: The water gets into the air gaps and air bubbles are pushed out to the surface.

Page 24 Revision Pages

Q1: Oxygen ———————— Filling balloons to make them go up.
Helium ———————— As fuel for cookers.
Carbon dioxide ———————— For divers to breathe underwater.
Natural gas ———————— To make soft drinks fizzy.

Q2: a) NO ✓

b) The water evaporates into the air.

Q3: Liquid evaporates into a vapour which you breathe in. As you breathe in you smell it.

Q4: You would only smell it after a while because it takes time for the vapour to spread through the air in the room and reach your nose.

Q5: ⟨Fumes from a tin of house paint.⟩   ⟨Vapour from a tube of glue.⟩
⟨Car exhaust fumes⟩ | Natural gas from a cooker. | Air.

Water vapour.   Vapour from perfume.   The fizz from

fizzy drinks.

Page 25 A Great Big Poster

Q1: Liquids change shape to fit the **CONTAINER** you put them in.
Liquids stay the same size — you can't **STRETCH** or squash them.
Liquids **FLOW** downwards easily.
The picture should show water flowing down out of the tap.

Q2: Solids keep their **SHAPE** when you put them in a different container.
Solids stay the same **SIZE**.
The picture should show any obviously plastic object.

Q3: Gases change their shape to **FILL** the container you put them in.
Gases expand to fill **BIGGER** spaces and can easily be squashed into **SMALLER** spaces.
Gases **FLOW** more easily than liquids and in all directions.
The picture should show gas flowing out of the jar in all directions.

KS2 Science Answers — Gases Around Us

Page 1 Differences Between Solids and Liquids

Q1:
SOLID	LIQUID
cake	soup
book	milkshake
rock	water

Q2: Will flow: MILKSHAKE, **SOUP**, **WATER**
Won't flow: **CAKE**, **BOOK**, **ROCK**
Will take the shape of the container...: MILKSHAKE, **SOUP**, **WATER**
Will keep its own shape when...: **CAKE**, **BOOK**, **ROCK**
Can be held between your fingers: **CAKE**, **BOOK**, **ROCK**
Can't be held between your fingers: MILKSHAKE, **SOUP**, **WATER**

Page 2 Air is Real

Q1: A substance all around you that you can't see ✓
Q2: Air
Q3: Air
Q4: a) It spins round
(a similar answer would do eg "It rotates" or " The sails go round") .
b) This answer should be circled: **The air pushes on the sails**

Page 3 Air is Real

Q1: a) more slowly
b) Because the air would be pushing up against the parachute ✓
Q2: a) I have a toy boat with sails in my garden pond. On a **STILL** day, the boat doesn't move. On a **WINDY** day, the boat moves really fast. That's because the **WIND** is pushing against the sails. Wind is just **AIR** that's moving.
b) More quickly
c) "Because bigger sails will have more wind pressing against them." should be circled.

Page 4 Air Has Weight

Q1: Air
Q2: Air is a **GAS** and it has **WEIGHT**. It's hard to notice this because air is very **LIGHT**. The experiment with the scales and balloons showed that air has weight, because the balloon with **AIR** squashed in it weighed **MORE** than the balloon with no air squashed in it.
Q3: The one crammed full of air weighs more.

Page 5 MINI-PROJECT Solids With Air In Them

Q1: Solid
Q2: Air ✓
Q3: Air

Page 6 MINI-PROJECT Solids With Air In Them

Q1: Bubbles should have been seen coming out of the sponge.
Q2: Air
Q3: Water

Page 7 MINI-PROJECT Solids With Air In Them

Q1: There should have been bubbles coming out while the water was poured onto the marbles, sand and soil and bubbles should have carried on coming out after the water was poured in to each of them.
Q2: Air
Q3: When you pour **WATER** onto marbles, it goes into the spaces and pushes out the **AIR**, which comes to the surface in **BUBBLES**. Powders like sand and soil are also made up of bits of solid with **AIR** between them. When you pour water on **POWDERS** it's the same as with marbles — bubbles of **AIR** are pushed out by the **WATER** and rise to the surface. The bubbles keep coming to the surface until all the **AIR** is pushed out.

Page 8 MINI-PROJECT Solids With Air In Them

Q1: This could be answered **YES** or **NO** and be correct.
Q2: ✓ Do the experiments again in the same way as before.
Q3: There should have been bubbles coming out while the water was poured onto the marbles, sand and soil and bubbles should have carried on coming out after the water was poured in to each of them.
Q4: The result should have been the same as before.

Page 9 MINI-PROJECT Solids With Air In Them

Q1: ✓ Because you might have made a mistake with the first experiment.
✓ If you get the same results twice, you can probably say you got the right results.
✓ If you get different results, you know you've done something wrong somewhere, so you need to do it a few more times to check.

Page 10 continued (right column)

Q2: Sponge experiment: This could be anything found out during the sponge experiment. Some examples - 1) that a sponge is full of holes, 2) that the holes in a sponge are full of air when it's dry, 3) you squeeze the air out of a sponge under water as bubbles, 4) if you squeeze a sponge and release it under water the holes fill with water.
The experiments with marbles, sand and soil: As above anything that they found out in the marbles, sand and soil experiment could be written in here. Some examples: 1) when you pour water on marbles / sand / soil the air comes out in bubbles, 2) after you have poured water on marbles / sand / soil the air continues to comes out in bubbles, 3) there are air spaces in marbles / sand / soil.

Page 10 Testing How Much Air Is In Soil

Q1: Pour water from a measuring jug onto the soil until the water reaches the 100ml mark and no more bubbles are coming out of the soil.

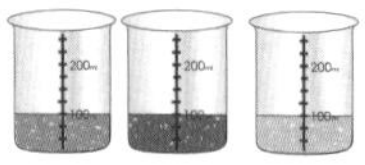

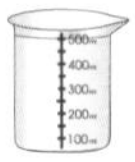

You should start with 500ml of water each time you begin pouring it on a soil. The amount of water that you poured in is the same as the amount of air that was in there before.

Q2: The first method should be ticked.

Page 11 How To Test How Much Air Is In Soil

Q1: The answers should be similar to those below although they can be worded differently.
(1) **The same amount of each type of soil was used (100ml).**
(2) **The same amount of water was used each time (500ml).**
(3) All beakers were the same shape and size.
Q2: Repeat it.
Q3: The fourth method should be ticked (or any suitable answer).

Page 12 Testing How Much Air Is In Soil

Q1: 10 ml
40 ml
20 ml
Q2: **Sandy soil has the most air. Clay soil has the least air.**
Clay soil has smaller gaps or fewer gaps.
Sandy soil has the largest gaps or most gaps.
Normal soil has smaller or fewer gaps than sandy soil and bigger or more gaps than clay soil.
The answer doesn't have to be worded exactly the same as this, but it has to get across that sandy soil has the biggest or most gaps (and most air), normal soil has the next biggest size or number of gaps and clay soil has the smallest or fewest gaps (and least air).
Q3: The answer should say something about breathing.

Page 13 Air

Q1:

Air

Okay, you already know that air is a <u>gas</u> — that's why you might not even notice it's there.
Even though you can't <u>see</u> it, air has <u>weight</u> and resists you when you move through it.
Let's see if you've got that all sorted...

Q1 Fill in this crossword about air.

Simon thought the
book said that *hair*
was a gas.

CLUES

Across
1) Humans need air to – – – – – – – .
4) A small parachute would fall – – – – – – than a big parachute.
5) Air is all around you but you can't – – – it.
6) Air does have weight but it is very – – – – – .
8) The holes in a dry sponge are full of – – – .
9) Does a balloon blown up with air weigh more or less than an empty one? – – – –

Down
2) A big parachute falls to earth slowly because of air – – – – – – – – – – .
3) If you squeeze a sponge in water then air – – – – – – – are pushed out.
7) Air is a – – – .

Air today — gone tomorrow...

OK, so you already know stuff about air. You know you can't see it, or smell it. And you know it's
a gas, and it does weigh something — just not very much. And it's what slows down parachutes.

Different Gases

Air isn't the <u>only</u> gas around — in fact there are <u>loads</u> of different gases.
We use gases a lot <u>every day</u>. Here are a few different ones along with some of their <u>uses</u>.

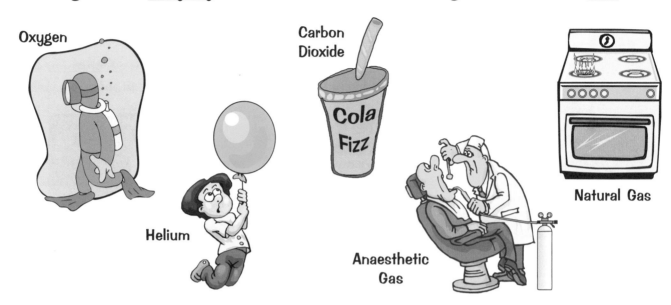

Oxygen

Helium

Carbon
Dioxide

Anaesthetic
Gas

Natural Gas

Q1   Take a look at these pictures, then write down next to each one which
of the gases from above is being used. Each gas is only used once.

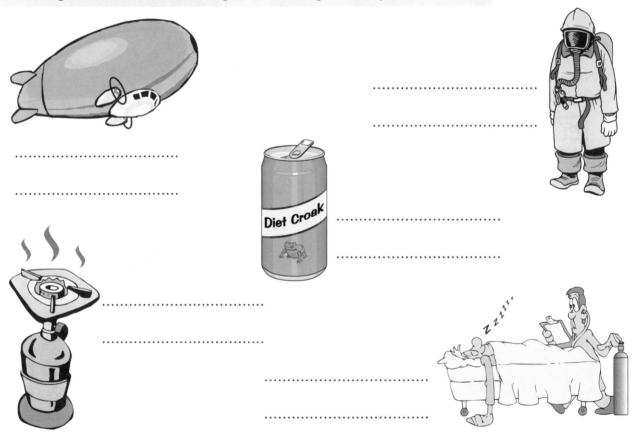

....

....

....

....

....

....

....

....

Diet Croak

How did Noel introduce his brother? — He Lium...

Air is a gas but it's not the only gas. Gases get used for loads of things all around us every day.
This page only has a few examples of different gases and their uses — there are masses more.

Oxygen

Lots of different gases are really useful. Oxygen is one of them
— the reason you breathe in air is because there's oxygen in it.

Q1   Read this passage carefully and then answer the questions about it.

> On this planet, there is more oxygen than any other chemical. More than half of our bodies are made up of oxygen, and almost all living things have oxygen in them. Oxygen has no taste, smell or colour, and it is an important part of water. It is produced by plants, and most animals breathe oxygen to stay alive. Pure oxygen is given to people who have trouble breathing, and also to people in high-flying aeroplanes or to deep-sea divers — anywhere where there's not enough oxygen.

a) What does oxygen taste like?

    ....

b) What is your body mostly made up of?

    ....

c) What makes oxygen?

    ....

Dave realised he'd picked
up the wrong bottles.

d) Name two situations where people need extra supplies of oxygen.

    1) ....

    2) ....

Bonus Question

Remember to
ask before you
use the Internet!

Bonus points if you can find out the answer to this
extra question. You could try looking in an <u>encyclopedia</u>,
or maybe you could look on the <u>Internet</u>.

Q2   Plants produce oxygen that they don't need as part of a process
they use to make food. What is the name of this process?

....

All around you, but you never see it — weird stuff, air...

Crikey — oxygen's pretty darned important stuff. It makes up more than half our bodies and
it's a vital part of water too. It does loads of things — so make sure you've learnt all of them.

Evaporation

Puddles disappear, and wet clothes dry in the sun.
It's because the <u>liquid water</u> turns into a <u>gas</u> — however strange that may sound.

Jeremy is trying an experiment with a puddle. After it has been raining, he goes
and measures the most impressive looking puddle. An hour later, he measures it again.
It's a bit smaller than before. After another hour, it's even smaller, and when he comes
back the next morning, the puddle has dried up completely.

After rain...   ...an hour later...   ...another   ...next day.
                                                    hour later...

Jeremy wants to know where the water has gone. He thinks it might have soaked
into the pavement. To test this idea, he decides to make his own puddle by pouring
water into something waterproof, so that the water won't sink through it.

Q1   Tick any of these containers which would be good for
      making a puddle in. (Hint: it has to be waterproof.)

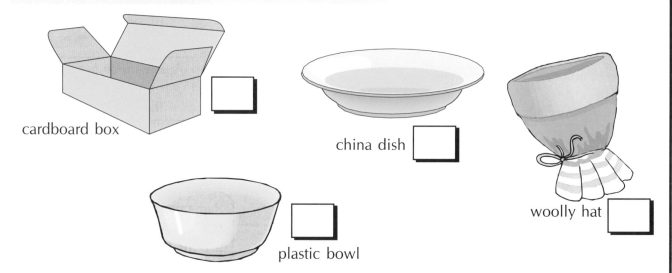

cardboard box

china dish

woolly hat

plastic bowl

Jeremy puts some water in a waterproof container and leaves it outside.
He comes back the next day and finds that the water has disappeared again.

Q2   Where do you think the water has gone?

      ....

Wat-er disaster — the puddle dried up...

Even though the water couldn't have been soaked up by the container, it had still gone. Try this
yourself if you like — but don't do it outside if it's likely to rain before you go and check the water.

Evaporation

**If a liquid 'dries up', it doesn't just disappear — it turns into a gas.
When this happens, it's called 'evaporation'.**

Q1 a) What happens to wet clothes when you hang
them up outside? (As long as it's not raining.)

....

....

   b) Why does this happen?
(Hint: What happens to the water on the clothes?)

....

....

....

Q2 a) When you hang your washing in a room and
shut the door, the air in the room gets damp.
What has happened to the water on the clothes?

....

....

Archie made sure he wouldn't
get damp when the water on
the clothes evaporated.

   b) Why do you think the air in the room gets damp?

....

....

Q3 Bertha had wet hair. Now that Pierre has used his hairdryer,
her hair is dry. What has happened to the water?

....

....

A vapour ate it? — No, it EVAPORATED...

Make sure you remember that water doesn't vanish when it evaporates. The water is still
there, in the air — but it has turned into a gas (a vapour). So the air gets a bit damper.

Smells

You smell things when a gas goes into your nose. When a liquid <u>evaporates</u>, it makes a <u>vapour</u>, which you breathe in. As you breathe it in, you can smell it.

Q1 Here are some pictures of liquids. You can smell some of them when part of the liquid evaporates (only a tiny bit of the liquid has to evaporate). Put a tick ✔ next to the ones you can smell.

Don't go sniffing these to find out. Sniffing paint fumes can be <u>dangerous</u>.

paint ☐   water ☐   hot chocolate ☐   perfume ☐

Q2 If I put a few drops of perfume onto a saucer and leave it overnight, what do you think will have happened to it by the morning?

....

....

Q3 I stood at one end of a big room, and my friend Jimbob stood at the other end with a bottle of perfume. He took the top off the bottle, and after a while I could smell the perfume.

a) Why couldn't I smell the perfume before he opened the bottle?

....

....

b) Why couldn't I smell the perfume as soon as he opened the bottle?

....

....

....

The new car for the 21st century — square wheels!

Design Plans

Ian's ideas really stank.

'My dog has no nose.' 'How does it smell?' 'Awful.'

We smell perfume because the liquid is evaporating once someone puts it on their skin. We smell the vapour from a hot drink too, even though not all the liquid evaporates — just a little bit of it.

Smells

It's not a good idea to breathe in any old gas. In fact, some are <u>dangerous</u> if you breathe them in. Steer clear of vapour from house paint or glue, and car exhaust fumes.

Q1 Why is it useful that some dangerous gases have a horrible smell? Put a tick ✔ next to the right answer.

Because everything that smells bad is dangerous. ....

So you can use them to annoy other people. ....

So you know they're there and can stop

yourself breathing any in. ....

Q2 Fill in the gaps in these sentences about gas being dangerous. Use some of the words in the cloud of smoke on the right.

Natural gas is .... if it leaks.

It .... really easily, so if a load of

gas leaked into a room and someone walked in and lit a

.... , it could cause an ....

If there was a gas leak in your house, you would

.... the gas and could get out of

the house and tell someone, so that the leak could be fixed.

smell explosion dangerous flood see match burns brown

Q3 Natural gas doesn't have a smell of its own. The nasty smell is added to it before the gas gets supplied to homes. Why do you think that is?

....

....

....

I'm outa here.

PONG

Doris's pet bird didn't like it when she painted the house.

Don't breathe in fumes — you'll be fuming...

Quite an important page, this. Try not to breathe in any paint or exhaust fumes. And if there <u>is</u> a gas leak, make sure you tell someone — and don't even think about lighting a match.

Solids, Liquids and Gases

The next few pages are all about solids, liquids and gases. <u>Solids</u> are dead boring and don't flow. <u>Liquids</u> can <u>flow</u> and change shape to <u>fit their container</u>. <u>Gases</u>, the lively little blighters, get absolutely everywhere 'cos they flow in <u>all directions</u>. Phew — hope you got all that.

Q1 These three syringes are filled with sand, water and air. I wanted to know what happens if I block one end with my finger and try to squash what's inside, so I've tried it out.

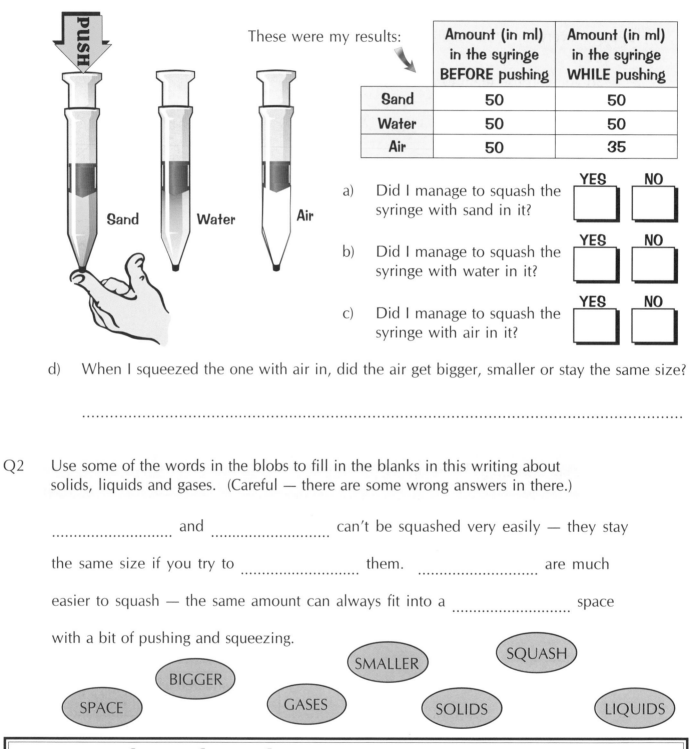

These were my results:

	Amount (in ml) in the syringe BEFORE pushing	Amount (in ml) in the syringe WHILE pushing
Sand	50	50
Water	50	50
Air	50	35

a) Did I manage to squash the syringe with sand in it?   YES ☐ NO ☐

b) Did I manage to squash the syringe with water in it?   YES ☐ NO ☐

c) Did I manage to squash the syringe with air in it?   YES ☐ NO ☐

d) When I squeezed the one with air in, did the air get bigger, smaller or stay the same size?

....

Q2 Use some of the words in the blobs to fill in the blanks in this writing about solids, liquids and gases. (Careful — there are some wrong answers in there.)

.... and .... can't be squashed very easily — they stay

the same size if you try to .... them. .... are much

easier to squash — the same amount can always fit into a .... space

with a bit of pushing and squeezing.

SMALLER   SQUASH   BIGGER   GASES   SOLIDS   SPACE   LIQUIDS

Squeezing air — it's easy peasy gas squeezy...

If you've got a plastic syringe in your classroom, get your teacher to show you this experiment. If you don't believe gases can be squashed up small, you can see it with your own eyes.

Solids, Liquids and Gases

This page is about how liquids and gases <u>move</u>.
Movement of a <u>liquid</u> or a <u>gas</u> in any direction is called <u>flow</u>.

Q1 a) I'm doing another experiment. I've got a bottle of water and another bottle filled with a purple gas, both laid on their sides.

What will the water and the gas do when I remove the lids?

The water will ....

The purple gas will ....

do a little dance

pour out all over the floor

turn green

stay where it is

flow out in all directions

b) Draw the water and the gas in the second pictures, after I've taken the lids off.

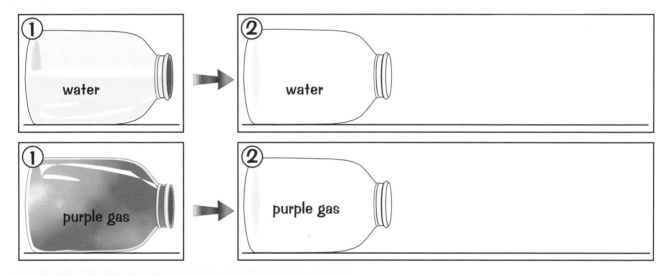

Q2 This time the bottles are both standing upright.

a) What will the water do when I remove the lid?

....

....

b) What will the gas do when I remove the lid?

....

....

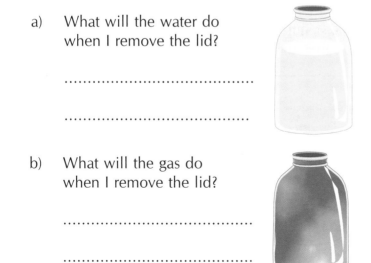

Ali wondered what would happen when she took the lid off the bottle.

Go with the flow...

OK, so it's easy to work out what happens to the water... the tricky bit is working out what the gas does. Gases and liquids are <u>different</u>. They don't always do the same thing as each other.

Solids, Liquids and Gases

This is the last experiment. I've got three bottles. One's filled with water, one's filled with purple gas and the other's got a wooden block in it.

I tip each bottle upside down into a groovy see-through plastic bucket. I take the bottle top off and shake the contents out. Then I shove the lid on top of the bucket.

Move it!

Bob knew the gas would move.

Wooden block

Water

Purple gas

Q1 What happens to the shape and size of the contents? On the three empty buckets on the right, draw the outlines of the wood, gas and water after they've been tipped out of the jars.

Wooden block

Purple gas

Water

Q2 a) Fill in the yellow columns of the table to say what happens to the size and shape of each one. I've done a couple to start you off.

	Change in Shape	Change in Size	Does it flow? If so, which direction?
Wood			
Purple Gas		*bigger*	
Water	*Fills bottom of bucket*		

b) Here are three things that happen when I empty the bottles into the buckets. Put each one into the right box in the green column.

Doesn't flow — just falls

Flows downwards

Flows in all directions

My hair's like a gas — it goes in all directions...

It's all starting to get a bit tricky, now. It's difficult to imagine how gases flow — but think of when you're outside and you see dust being blown about on the air. It goes just about everywhere.

Revision Pages

Tons of great questions for you here — but don't panic.
You've covered all this stuff in the book already, so look back at other pages if you really need to.

Q1   What is air? Tick ✔ the right answer.

A substance that you can see
and pick up with your hand.   ☐

A substance all around
you that you can't see.   ☐

Q2   Fill in the blanks in these sentences. Use all the words from the boat.

Captain Birdsfeet is sailing his boat. On a .... day,

the boat doesn't move. On a .... day, the boat

moves really fast. That's because the .... is pushing

against the sails. Wind is just .... that's moving.

still
windy
wind   air

Q3   Fill in the blanks in these sentences, using the words in the brackets.

Air is a .... (gas / liquid) and it has .... (weight / colour). It's

hard to notice this because air is very .... (heavy / light). A balloon with air

squashed in it weighs .... (less / more) than one with no air squashed in it.

Q4   Fill in the labels on the diagram using some of the words on the right.

....

....

sponge

air
        soil

nothing

milk

Q5   (Circle) the sentence that describes what happens when you pour water onto soil.

The water stays
on top of the soil.

The water gets into the air
gaps and air bubbles are
pushed out to the surface.

The soil melts
because it's hot.

It's all a lot of hot air if you ask me...

All this revision stuff is dead useful — it's no use doing all that work if you forget it straight away.
And even better — there are loads more questions on the next page. So get stuck in and enjoy...

Revision Pages

One page down, two to go. Don't give up yet — it's just starting to get interesting...

Q1   Here's a list of gases, and a list of things you'd use the
       gases for. Draw a line to match each gas with its use.

Oxygen   Filling balloons to make them go up.

Helium   As a fuel for cookers.

Carbon dioxide   For divers to breathe underwater.

Natural gas   To make soft drinks fizzy.

Q2 a) When wet clothes dry, or puddles dry   Yes [ ]   No [ ]
        up, does the water just disappear?

    b) If not, what happens
        to the water?   ....

                           ....

                           ....

Q3   How do you smell things? (Hint: it's to do with evaporation.)

       ....

       ....

Smelling method
no. 42.

Q4   If someone opens a bottle
       of aftershave at the other   ....
       end of the room, would you
       smell it straight away or   ....
       only after a while? Why?
                                        ....

Q5   (Ring) the gases which are   **Fumes from a tin of house paint.**   **Vapour from perfume.**
       dangerous to breathe in.
       Draw a [box] around the   **Air.**   **Car exhaust fumes.**   **The fizz from
       gas that's dangerous   fizzy drinks.**
       because it can explode.   **Natural gas
                                     Water vapour.   from a cooker.**   **Vapour from
                                                                              a tube of glue.**

Re-vision — when you see things over again...

This is kinda cool — it's called per<u>fume</u> and it's the <u>fumes</u> from it that you smell. I guess that's
where the word originally came from. Science brings up such fascinating facts... Well, it amused me.

A Great Big Poster

So, here it is — what you've all been waiting for... the last page.
Finish off this groovy poster by using the instructions in the yellow stars.

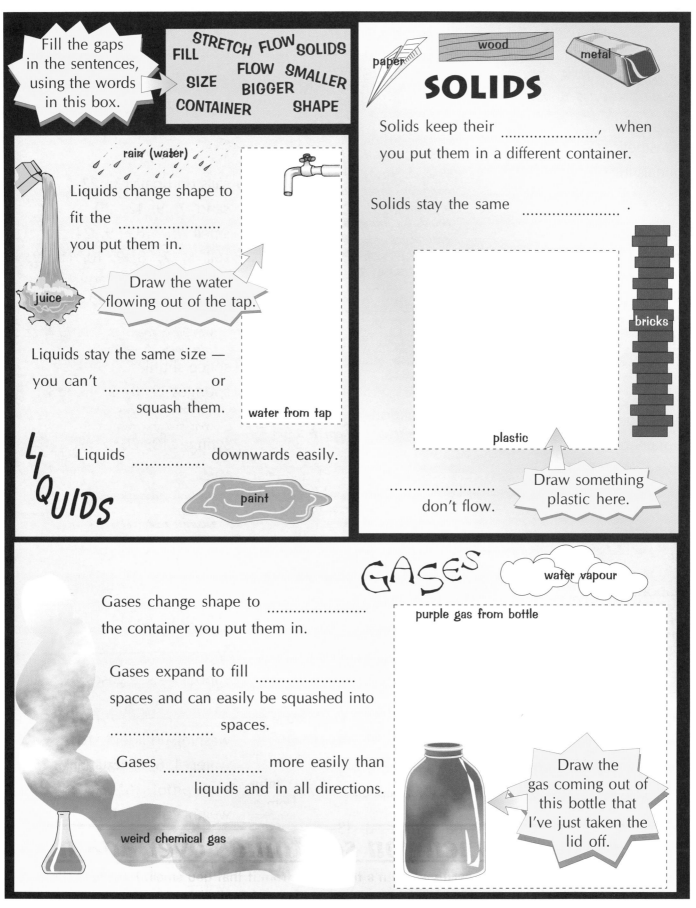

Fill the gaps in the sentences, using the words in this box.

STRETCH FLOW SOLIDS
FILL
FLOW SMALLER
SIZE BIGGER
CONTAINER SHAPE

SOLIDS

wood   metal   paper

Solids keep their ...., when you put them in a different container.

Solids stay the same ....

bricks

plastic

.... don't flow.

Draw something plastic here.

rain (water)

Liquids change shape to fit the .... you put them in.

Draw the water flowing out of the tap.

juice

Liquids stay the same size — you can't .... or squash them.

water from tap

LIQUIDS

Liquids .... downwards easily.

paint

GASES

water vapour

purple gas from bottle

Gases change shape to .... the container you put them in.

Gases expand to fill .... spaces and can easily be squashed into .... spaces.

Gases .... more easily than liquids and in all directions.

Draw the gas coming out of this bottle that I've just taken the lid off.

weird chemical gas

Index